LOBSTERS ON THE LOOSE

A COLLECTION OF CRUSTACEAN CARTOONS

BY JEFF PERT

Copyright 2015 by Jeff Pert
All rights reserved

ISBN 978-1-4951-4406-6

Entertain Ya MANIA

www.entertainyamania.com

Printed in Italy

FOR JEFF. THANKS FOR THE LAUGHS.

WAIT A MINUTE!!
THAT'S BILL!!
PERT

HELP!
PERT

LARRY? LISTEN, I'M GONNA BE A LITTLE LATE. I'VE GOT A SITUATION HERE...
©PEFT

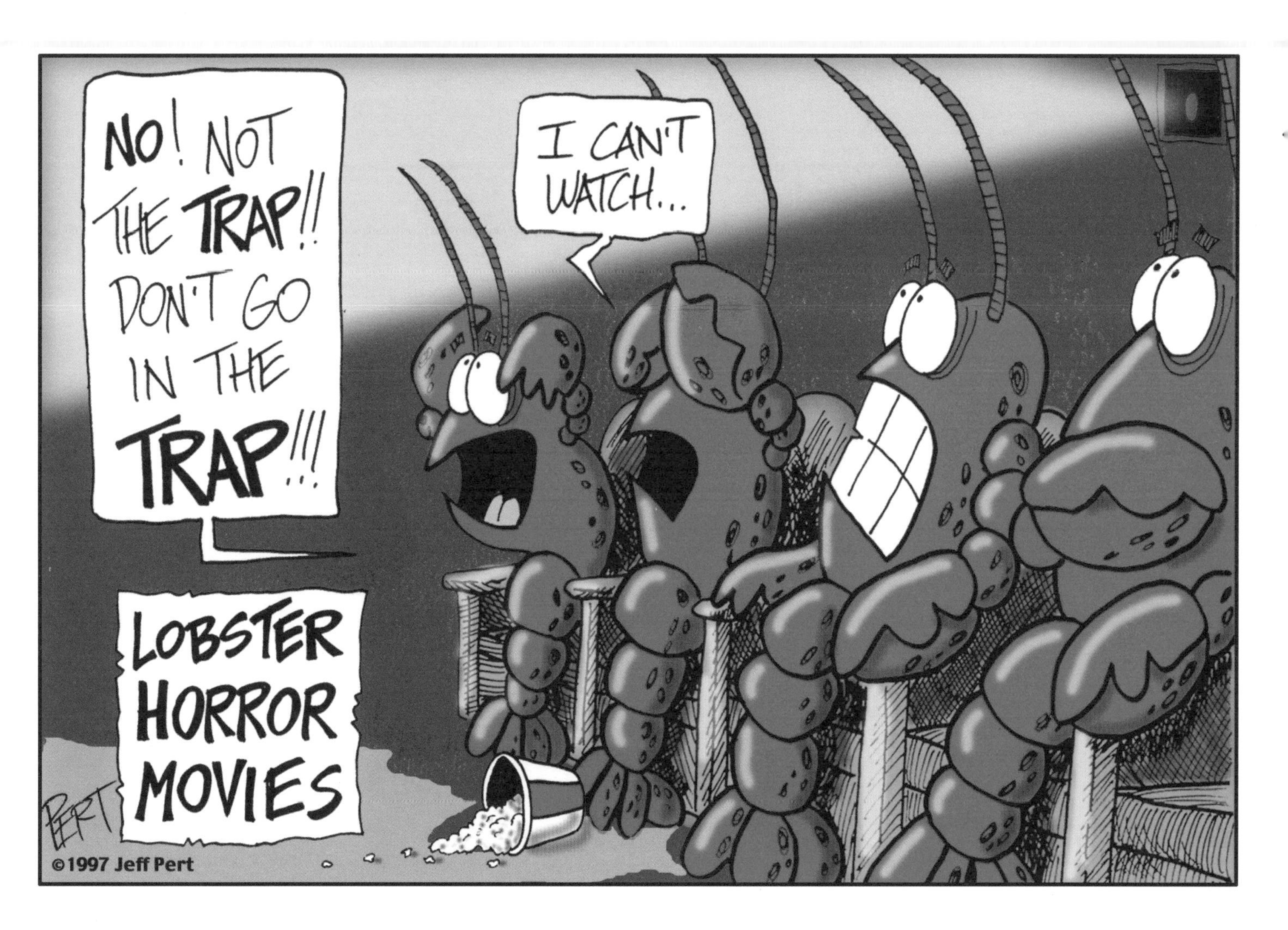
NO! NOT THE TRAP!! DON'T GO IN THE TRAP!!!
I CAN'T WATCH...
LOBSTER HORROR MOVIES
PERT
©1997 Jeff Pert

NO, I DON'T THINK IT'S COOL YOUR GPS SHOWS YOU RIGHT WHERE WE ARE!
PEPT

HOW NOT TO EAT A LOBSTER
PERT
©2006 Jeff Pert
WHAM!
With a hammer...
HEY– YOU GONNA EAT THAT!? CAN I HAVE SOME?? HUH? CAN I!? CAN I!?
Near a seagull...
SPLAT!
CRACK!
Without a bib...
Raw...
With chopsticks...
With a straw...

©1996 Jeff Pert
PERT
SURE DO MISS MY BABY!
MY BABY'S GONE – IT'S TOO LATE.
SHE DIED IN A GREAT BIG
POT OF SCALDING WATER,
THEN SHE DONE GONE
AND GOT ATE!
LOBSTER
BLUES

BOILED ALIVE AND EATEN– LIKE ALL THE OTHERS.
LOOKS LIKE A SERIAL KILLER'S LOOSE!
CRIME SCENE –
NOT CROSS – CR
LOBSTER CSI
PERT
©2005 Jeff Pert

BUD HAD FORGOTTEN THE FIRST RULE OF LOBSTERING: NEVER TURN YOUR BACK ON THE LOBSTERS...

OH YEAH, BUDDY?! WHY DON'T YOU JUST EAT ME!?
THINGS DRUNK LOBSTERS SHOULD NEVER SAY

THE LOBSTER TRAP RESTAURANT
SERIOUSLY!? THIS IS WHERE YOU WANT TO EAT??
SPECIALS
KARAOKE!
©HEY BOB, INC.

Click here to increase your claw size.
LOBSTER SPAM

WILL WORK FOR BAIT
PERI

YOU GONNA TALK, OR YOU WANT WE SHOULD BREAK OUT THE MELTED BUTTER!?
LOBSTER MOBS
PERT
©2004 Jeff Pert All rights reserved

GOTTA BE STEROIDS...
PEPT
CLAW ENVY

HOLD ON, I NEED TO TAKE THIS...
PERT

LOBSTER: EXPENSIVE and MESSY!!
BEEF MORE MEAT FOR THE $
BAN BOILING WATER
CHICKENS ARE STUPID! EAT THEM!
PERT

SINGLE CRUSTACEAN
w/ hard exterior but soft inside. Likes long walks in the ocean & dining on dead, rotten fish. Calm, not quick to boil. Seeks companion w/ a nice tail.
THE WEEKLY BRINE
LOBSTER PERSONAL ADS
PERT

HAPPY NEW YEAR, EVERYBODY!!
YOU STILL DON'T GET IT, DO YOU, STEVE?
LIVE LOBSTER
$6 99/lb.
PEART

A GLASS OF BRINE, PLEASE!
LEMME GUESS— YOU'RE A CANCER! AM I RIGHT?
LOBSTER BARS

I'M WITH STUPID
©2006 Jeff Pert
PERT

I'M THINKING ABOUT HEADING SOUTH FOR THE SUMMER. LESS CHANCE OF BEING EATEN BY A TOURIST...
PERT

GATES
ARRIVALS
LIVE LOBSTERS PACKED TO TRAVEL

Y'KNOW? SOME CURTAINS, A COUCH, A LITTLE PAINT— THIS PLACE WOULDN'T BE HALF BAD!
YOU STILL DON'T GET IT, DO YOU, DORIS?

WHADDAYA MEAN YOU DON'T HAVE ANY CHOCOLATE-COVERED HERRING EYES!? YOU CALL THIS A CONCESSION STAND!?!
WHEN LOBSTERS GO TO THE MOVIES
BERT

GLUB! CAN'T SWIM!! THROW ME A LINE!!!
YOU'RE AN IDIOT, YOU KNOW THAT?!
BERT

SUDDENLY, CHUCK REALIZED HIS "FRIENDS" HAD AN ULTERIOR MOTIVE FOR GETTING HIM IN THE HOT TUB...
PERT
©2001 Jeff Pert

HONEST! LET ME GO, AND I'LL SHOW YOU WHERE THERE'S THOUSANDS MORE JUST LIKE ME!

WHEN LOBSTERS SQUEAL

©2004 Jeff Pert
All rights reserved

www.entertainyamania.com

TWO HORSESHOE CRABS WALK INTO AN OYSTER BAR...
STAND-UP CRUSTACEAN

OOOH! MY NOSE!! MY NOSE!!
SOMEBODY SCRATCH MY NOSE!
LIVE LOBSTER
PEIRT

HA, HA. VERY FUNNY.
LOBSTER GAG GIFTS
PEAT

LOBSTER DREAMS
PERT

TAN LOTION
BOILED LOBSTER

THESE ☆#$!⚡ BUTTONS ARE TOO SMALL FOR MY CLAWS!!
WHEN LOBSTERS TEXT

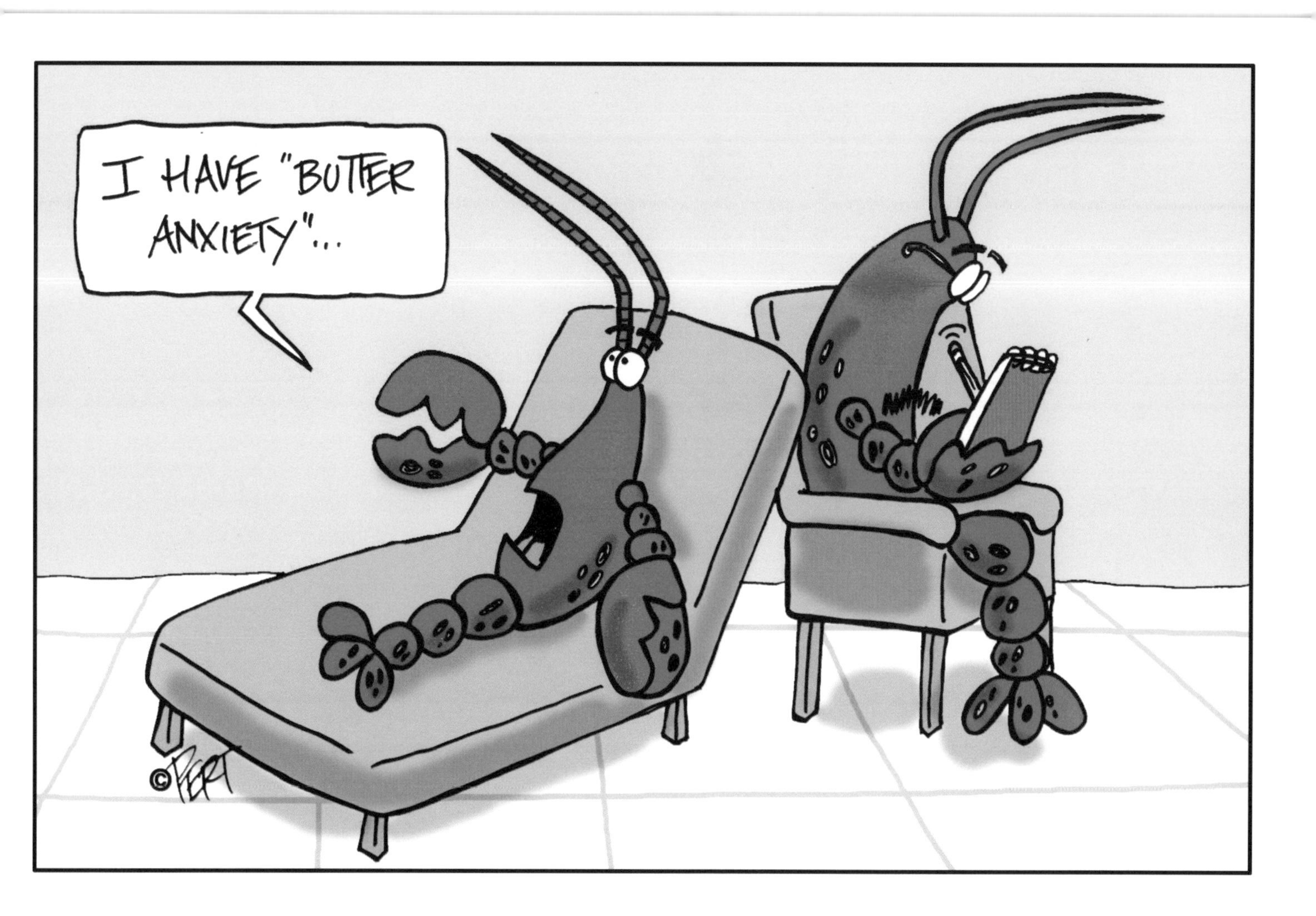
I HAVE "BUTTER ANXIETY"...
©PERT

HEY, AL! YOU'RE NEVER GONNA GUESS WHO I'M SITTING NEXT TO! THOSE LOSERS WHO ALMOST TRAPPED US LAST WEEK! NO, SERIOUSLY!
PEET

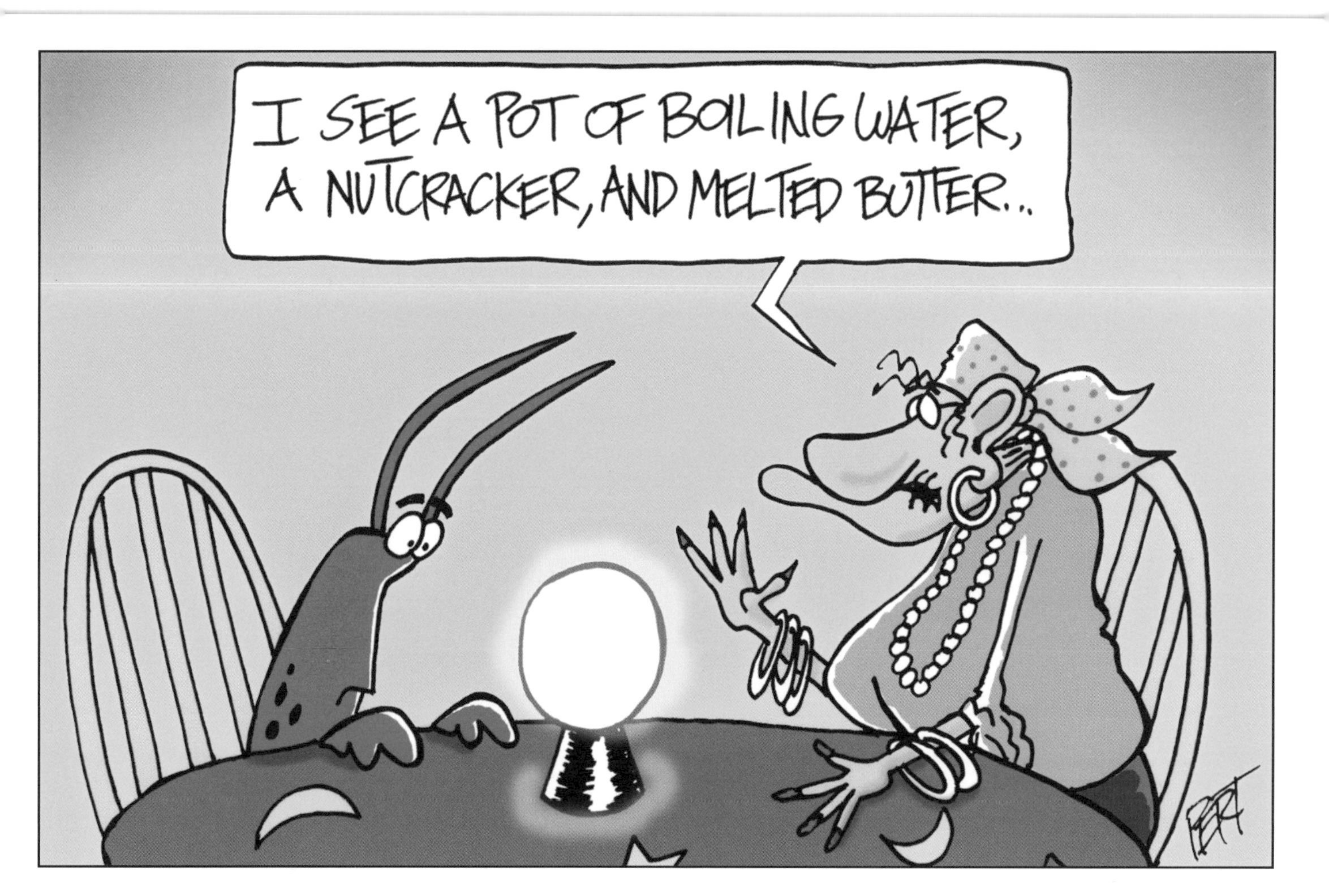
I SEE A POT OF BOILING WATER, A NUTCRACKER, AND MELTED BUTTER...
BERT

...AND A BIG, HONKIN' STOCKING FULL OF DEAD, ROTTEN POGIES!!
BERT

SURE, SURE. THE OL' "GOTTA-GET-BACK-TO-SALT-WATER-REALLY-QUICK" EXCUSE. TELL IT TO THE JUDGE!
PERT

©PERT
THERE'S ONE!!
THERE'S GOTTA BE A BETTER WAY...
THE DAY BEFORE THE INVENTION OF THE LOBSTER TRAP

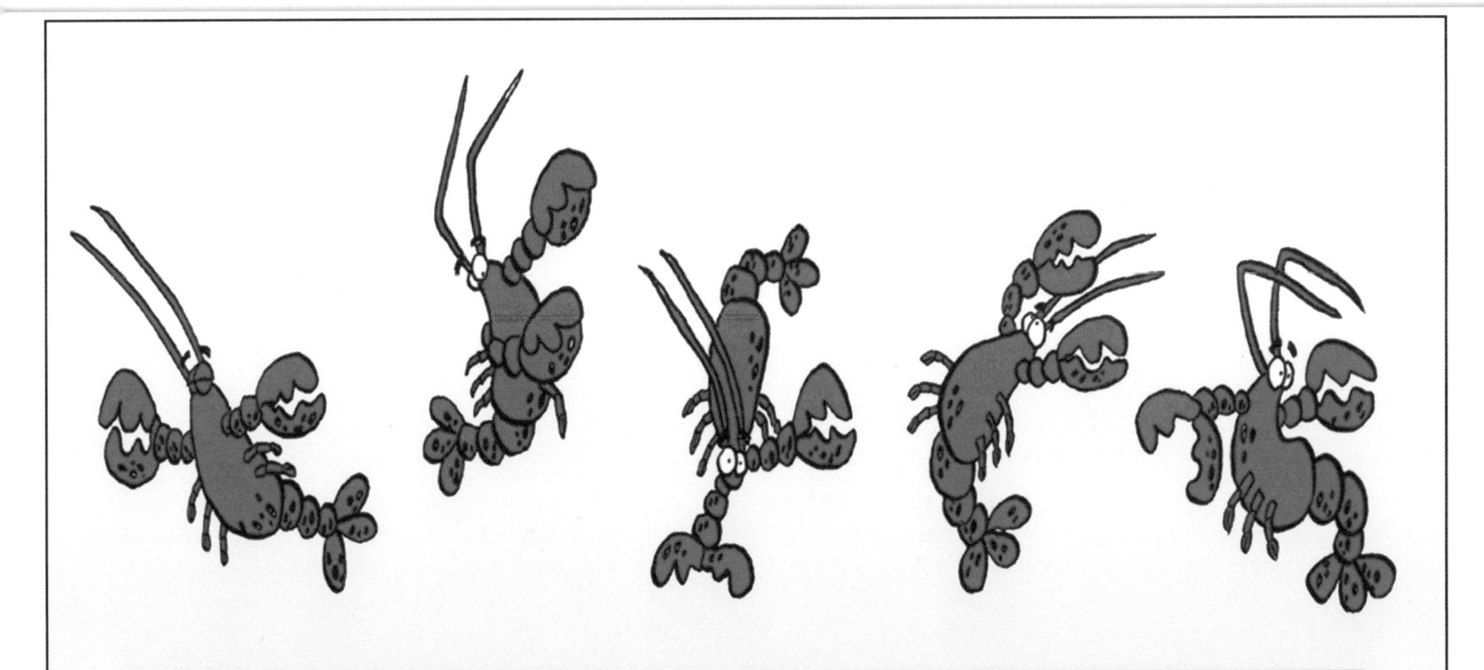

DANCES WITH LOBSTERS

LET'S DO IT— RIGHT HERE, RIGHT NOW!
YOU'RE SICK! NOW, TAKE ME!!
Fifty Shades of RED
PERT
© Hey Bob, Inc.

RELAX. ALL LOBSTERS HAVE ONE BIGGER THAN THE OTHER.
PEET
©HEY BOB, INC.

ARE YOU SURE THIS IS WHAT THEY CALL "HOT TUBBING"?!
©PERT

WE'RE ALL GONNA DIE!! DIE, I TELL YOU!!
GEEZ, DAVE— GET A GRIP!

I'M STONED OUT OF MY SHELL!
LOBSTER POT
© HEY BOB, INC.

DON'T YOU HAVE THESE IN ANYTHING BESIDES BLUE?!
©PEIRCE

©PERT
C'MON, BABY! PAPA NEEDS A BRAND NEW PAIR OF SHOES!
LOBSTER ROLL

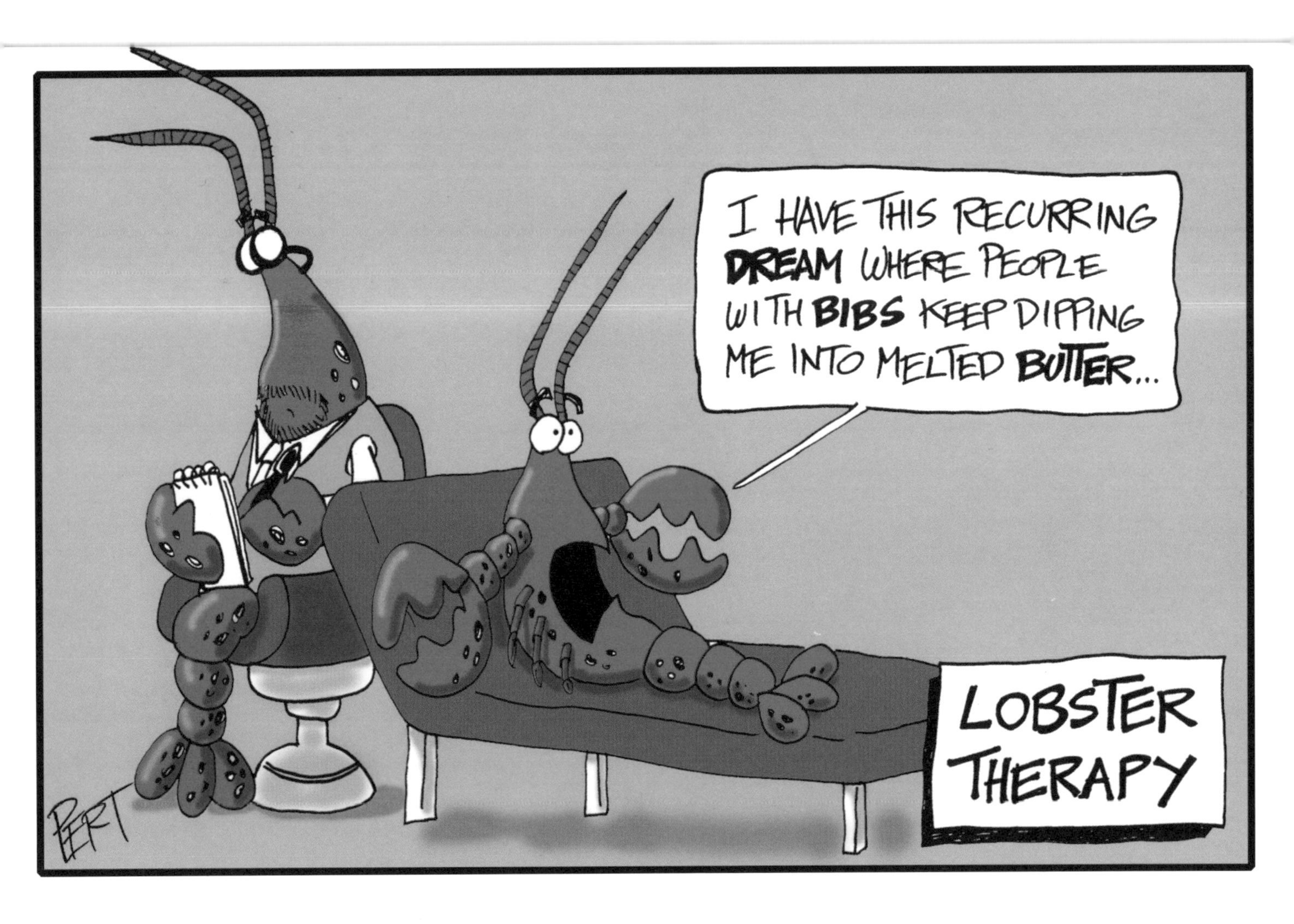
I HAVE THIS RECURRING DREAM WHERE PEOPLE WITH BIBS KEEP DIPPING ME INTO MELTED BUTTER...
LOBSTER THERAPY
PERT

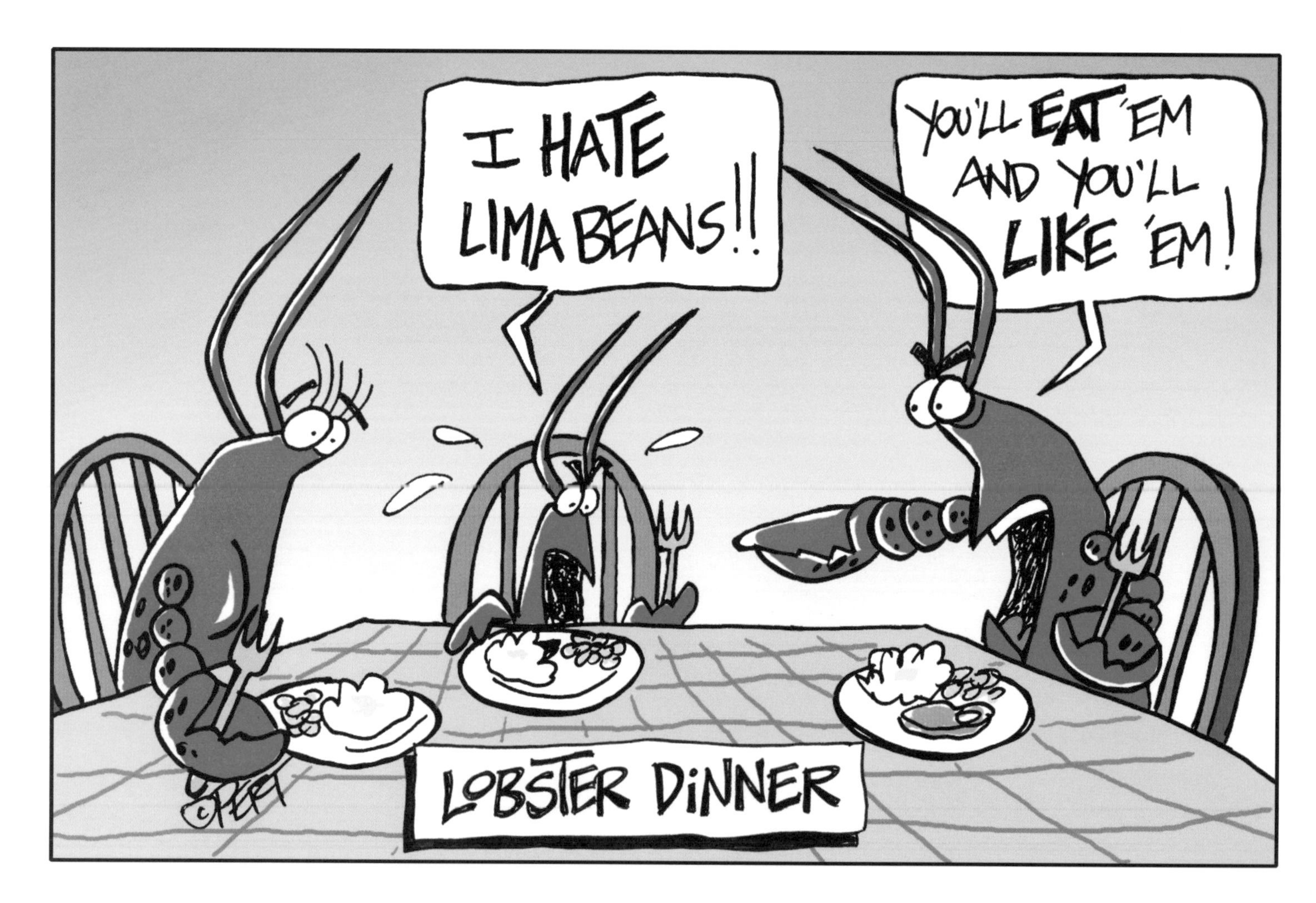
I HATE LIMA BEANS!!
YOU'LL EAT 'EM AND YOU'LL LIKE 'EM!
LOBSTER DINNER
©PERT

CRUSTACEAN INEBRIATION
PERT
©2006 Jeff Pert

WELL, AIN'T YOU THE CUTEST WIDDLE THING?! YES YOU ARE! YES YOU ARE!
PEET
IT BECAME CLEAR THE NEW GUY WASN'T GOING TO WORK OUT...

WHO FARTED?
LIVE LOBSTERS
©PERT

©2005 Jeff Pert

LATELY I'VE FELT TRAPPED...

BACK AWAY FROM THE STOVE, PUT SHIRLEY ON THE COUNTER, AND NO FAST MOVES!!
BERT

OOH, ME!!
PICK ME!
LOBSTERS THAT DON'T GET IT...
©PEART

HEY, BOB! HOW'S THE WATER? BOB? BOB!? BOB!!
PERT
©1999 Jeff Pert